THE HOFFNUNG MUSIC FESTIVAL

By the Author of

THE MAESTRO
THE HOFFNUNG SYMPHONY ORCHESTRA
THE HOFFNUNG COMPANION TO MUSIC
HOFFNUNG'S MUSICAL CHAIRS
HOFFNUNG'S ACOUSTICS

The Hoffnung Music Festival

by

Gerard Hoffnung

SOUVENIR PRESS

First published 1956 by Dennis Dobson

This edition first published 1983 by Souvenir Press Ltd, 43 Great Russell Street, London WC1B 3PA

Reprinted November 1983
Reprinted November 1985
Reprinted September 1988
Reprinted October 1991

ISBN 0 285 62613 2

Printed and bound in Spain by Printeksa, S.A.

To

The Morley College Symphony Orchestra
and its inspired conductor Lawrence
Leonard, with much affection.

The Conductors

Alerto

Preciso

Con adornamento

Grandioso

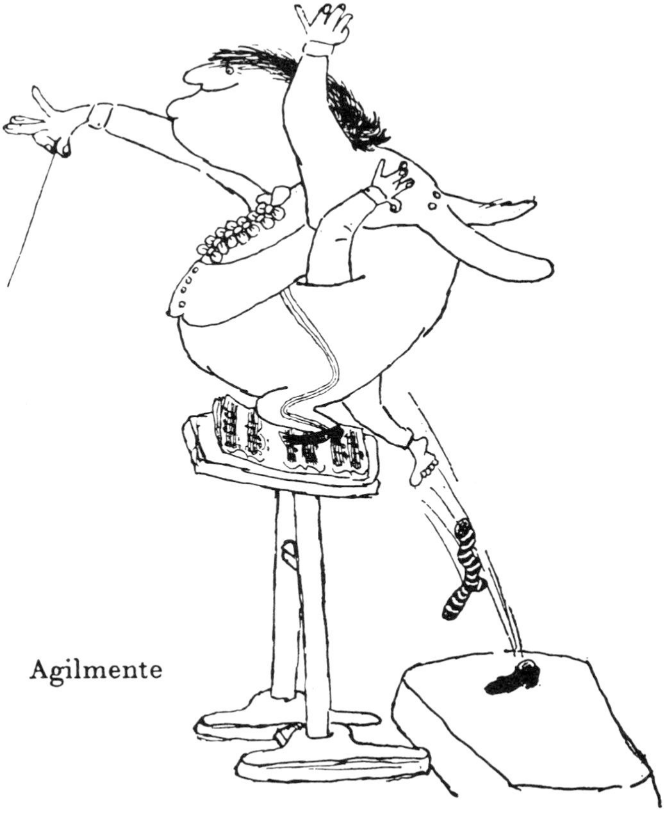

Agilmente

Piano

Con fuoco

Senza batone

Slargando

Maestoso

Non troppo

Elegantemente

Sehr markiert

Sotto

Bel Canto

on
off
Sobs
ppp
fff
wobble

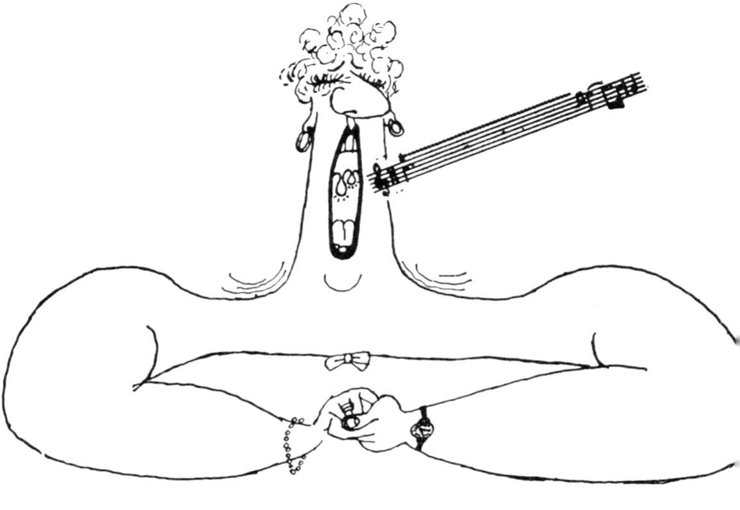

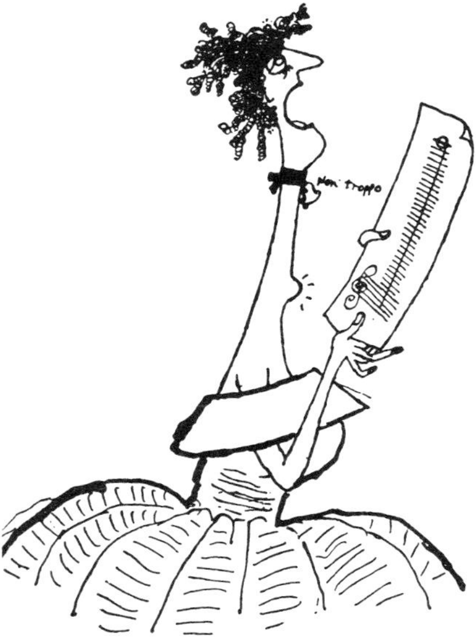

Coloratura

Basso

The Flower Song

Signorina. . .
acknowledges
applause

A sextet

The Festival Chorus

The Soloists

T.V. brings the Festival to a wider audience

An unfortunate incident

Billiards
Sonata:
Haydn

Introduzione
Affrettando
Finale

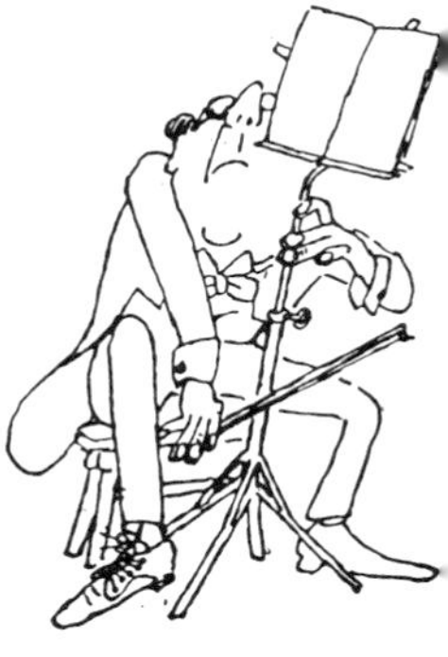

Mainly Instrumental

The TROUT
TROUT
TROUT

The Trout Quintet

VACUUM QUARTET IN A FLAT
(THE HOOVER)

for
two vacuums in f
one vacuum in E flat*
one contra vacuum in BB flat
(World première)

*If desired this may be replaced by an electric Floor-polisher in A flat.

Hoffnung

EXIT
„Haydn's
Surpri
Symph

Con Sord*

* with mute

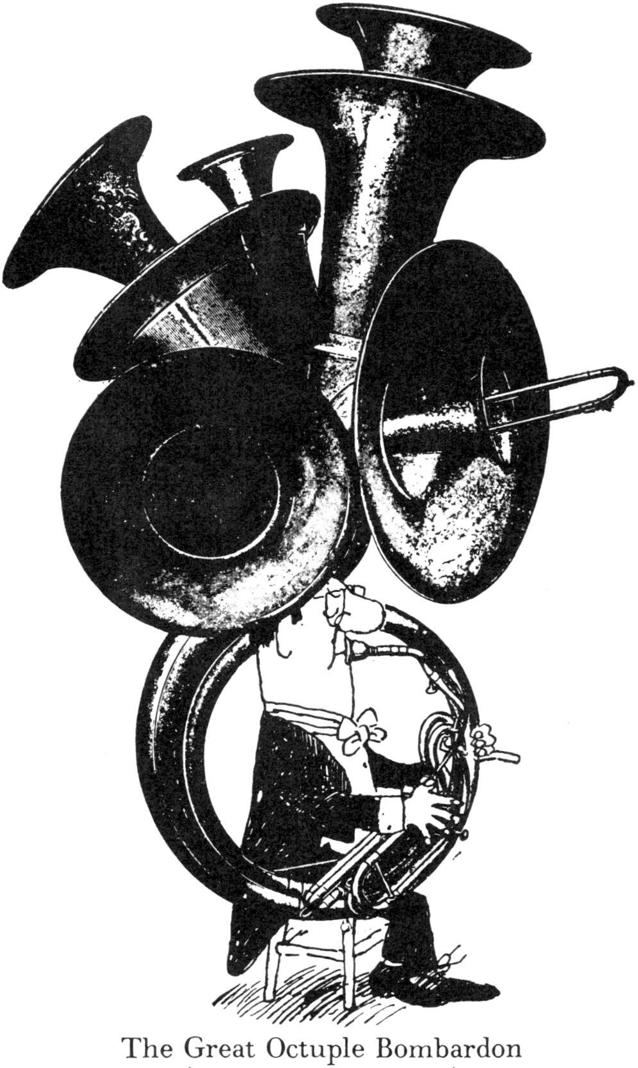

The Great Octuple Bombardon
(Americano Expresso)

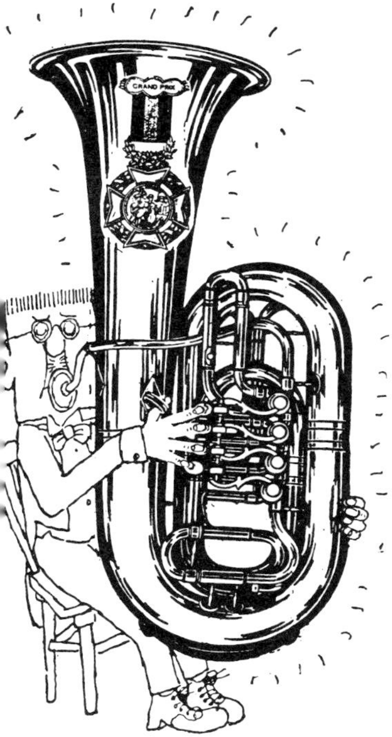

Tuba alla Tedesca

Tuba Anglais
(Leeds)

A bbb flat sub-contra-
bass-trombone-player
and friend

350 Bars Rest

Hoffnung

Help!!!
Hoffnung

THE END